colour in classics

JUP

Draw something fierce here...

Big Bad Wolf

Into the woods

Crowning glory

Sketch some fearless crows...

As the crow flies

Cinderella—dressing up

Rumpelstiltskin—the arrival

Draw someone spinning yarn...

Rumpelstiltskin—in a spin

Now sketch a baby's face...

Rumpelstiltskin—final demand

Draw a happy story ending...

Rumpelstiltskin—the big reveal

The Frog King

A thorny silence

Design some hats here...

Old hat

A dog's life

The Fisherman—caught in the act

Rapunzel—tower of strength

Rapunzel—window of opportunity

Now sketch a startled face...

Rapunzel—hair-raising!

Rapunzel—fall out of favor

Draw something feathery here...

Flight of fancy

Now create a woodland scene...

Branching out

Design your own quilt here...

A yarn to spin

Floundering around

Rapunzel—climb down

Snow White—open house

Draw someone peddling apples...

Snow White—the Big Apple!

Sketch your own dreamy character...

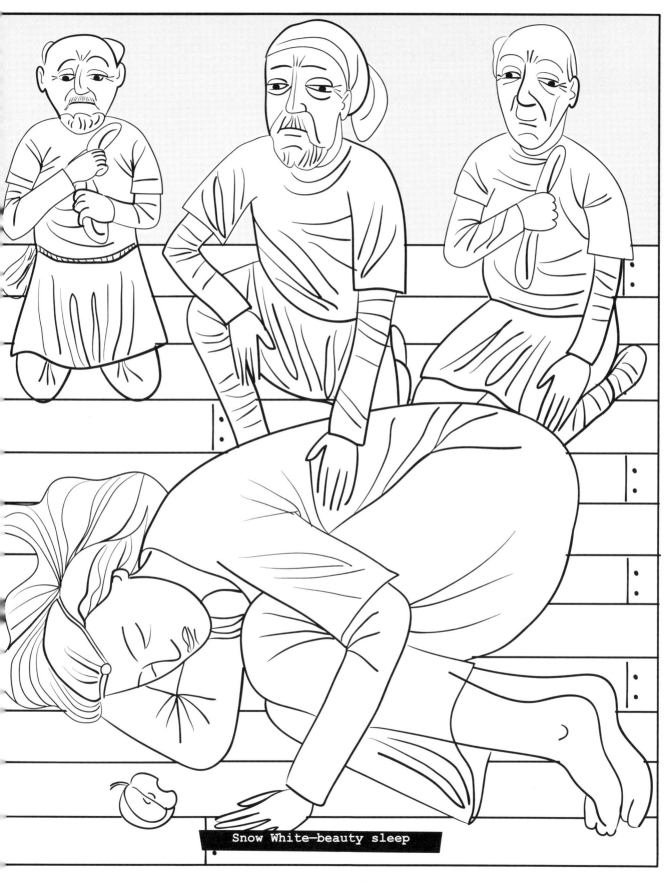

Snow White—beauty sleep

Snow White—wake up call

Rapunzel's bad hair day

Street life

Smelling of roses

Sketch some heroic leaping frogs...

Pond life

Red Riding Hood—basket case

Sleeping Beauty—born free

Sleeping Beauty—old wives' tale

Now sketch someone snoozing...

Sleeping Beauty—sleep tight

Sleeping Beauty—beauty spot

Draw something pretty here...

Hoodwinked!

Now create a traveling scene...

Cruise control

Scissor happy!

Sketch some majestic owls...

Night owls

Rumpelstiltskin—straw deal

Hansel and Gretel—off the trail

Draw someone in the dark woods...

Hansel and Gretel—sweet cottage

Now sketch an evil face...

Hansel and Gretel—lockdown

Hansel and Gretel—free at last

A cut above the rest

Now create a tall scene...

Tall order

Ax to grind

Sketch some graceful flying swans...

Swan song

Sleeping Beauty—throne away

Invent your own imaginary scene...

Red Riding Hood—red alert

Draw someone running scared...

Red Riding Hood—hungry like a wolf

Now sketch a wolf face...

Red Riding Hood—devil in disguise

Red Riding Hood—side-splitting

Drama queen

Swan lake

If the shoe fits...

Cry wolf!

Snow White—dinner service

Cinderella—pickup tricks

Draw someone daydreaming...

Cinderella—stairway to heaven

Cinderella—it fits!

Draw something scary here...

The evil eye

Now create a dark forest scene...

Oh deer!

Sweet memories

Birds of a feather

Hansel and Gretel—cottage industry

Design your own basket here...

Weave in and out

Now create a majestic garden scene...

Green as grass

Jumped Up Publishing
Bookspeed, 16 Salamander Yards, Edinburgh, EH6 7DD
www.bookspeed.com

Copyright © 2015  Paperwasp

Jumped Up Publishing is an imprint of Bookspeed, used with permission from
Jumped Up Publishing Ltd. All notations of errors or omissions should be
addressed to JUP at the above address.

All other correspondence (author inquiries, permissions) concerning the
content of this book should be addressed to Paperwasp at the address below.

This book was conceived, designed, and produced by Paperwasp,
an imprint of Balley Design Limited, The Loft, 45 Grantham Road,
Brighton, East Sussex, BN1 6EF, UK.
www.paperwaspbooks.com

Creative Director: Simon Balley
Designer: Kevin Knight
Text: Simon Balley
Illustrations: Kevin Knight and Martin Gordon
Cover: UyUy/Shutterstock.com and Kevin Knight
Publisher: Lewis Dawson
Editorial Team: Annie Rhodes and Shona Rowan

British Library cataloguing-in-Publication Data.
A catalogue record for this book is available from the British Library.

ISBN-13: 978-0-955364-14-3

Printed in China

19 18 17 16 15   1 2 3 4 5